UNCLE GLENI
ZOMBIE 'POCALYPSE

An Adult Coloring Adventure

MW00638214

UNCLE GLENNY'S ZOMBIE 'POCALYPSE

An Adult Coloring Adventure

Artwork by Glenn Chadbourne

Concept by Dave Hinchberger
and Glenn Chadbourne

OVERLOOK CONNECTION PRESS

Uncle Glenny's Zombie 'Pocalypse
An Adult Coloring Adventure

© 2016 by Glenn Chadbourne and Dave Hinchberger

Cover & interior Illustrations © 2016 by Glenn Chadbourne

© 2016 by Overlook Connection Press

Published © 2016 by
Overlook Connection Press
PO Box 1934, Hiram, Georgia 30141
www.overlookconnection.com
overlookcn@aol.com

Published in Three States:

Trade Paperback	ISBN: 9781623300753
Hardcover	ISBN: 9781623300784
Signed Limited Edition	ISBN: 9781623300920

All rights reserved. no part of this book may be reproduced or transmitted in any form or by any means, electronic or mechanical, without the written permission of the Publisher, Overlook Connection Press.

Why I Love Zombies

I love zombies. I've loved them in all their many forms since I was a carpet crawler (or, "youngwun" as they say up in this neck of the woods) when they first shambled into view on our old RCA console tube in the family living room by way of grainy films from the thirties and forties. White Zombie with uber creepy Bela Lugosi working a herd of them on his island plantation was... I'm thinking, the first such flick I ever saw. They staggered around, wall-eyed and moaning, powered by weird voodoo rites. There were a host of these sorts of flicks featured on Saturday creature features on the local channels, and I chewed through a steady diet of them, flounced on our groovy green shag carpet in my pj,s. I was perhaps eight or nine at the time. By the time I reached "tweenhood" I considered myself fairly well acquainted with that particular genre of the undead; through movies of course, but also in no small measure through stacks of comics and the great old Warren magazines of the day "Creepy, Eerie, Vampirela (you called her 'Vampy' if you were in the know—and she was smokin' hot) . The seventies arfed out an absolute slew of zombies on the screen. Hammer made the great gothic entry, "Plague of the Zombies," and the Italian splattermeisters helmed a whole subgenre genre via the creeping dead, too many to list and all over the top in gore-drenched splendor. There seemed to be one single guy who did all the voice-over English translations for these and he must've stayed busy for years. Of course George Romero served up the most famous humdinger classic of all in the late sixties (with equally cool sequels to follow), "Night of the Living Dead," and I remember they showed it on an old style movie screen in our high school cafeteria every Halloween.

Now, I enjoyed the hell out of all these movies; still rewatch them from time to time on DVD, but I can't honestly say any of them really scared me. Searching back through my brainball though, I do recall a couple that really got me—and that stayed with me creep-wise. One was from the TV pilot movie for Night Gallery. It was the segment with Roddy McDowell where, long story short, a murdered uncle crept from his grave and trudged toward the family mansion for revenge. His progress was shown through a series of paintings on a wall and the paintings kept changing to show his advance. That spooked me. Another one is a William Castle flick called "The Night Walker." That one starred Barbara Stanwyck. Barb's mad scientist husband blew himself up in an attic lab and returned to visit her from time to time in very unsettling ways. That one crawled over me big time. (You can't find it on DVD though—god knows I've tried). Anyway, I'm hooting away on all this stuff. Down to the book in your hands. I've tried to get across in this rambling preamble that zombies have been around for awhile, and that they only seem to be gaining a greater presence in day to day life. I'm told, even the army has drawn up mock war plans for a zombie apocalypse scenario for fun. This is in no small part due to the phenomenal success of the TV show "The Walking Dead." A show that's brought brain chowing to a wider audience than perhaps ever before, and caused terms associated with the Z-boys and girls to be entered into the English language lexicon. I figure all that deserves a nifty coloring book! Now, one last little note before you start having fun with your crayons. This book was tougher for me to lay out than most books I'm involved with, because it's very hard for me to ease off the throttle with detail. I'm used to performing micro surgery with jillions of little squiggly pen strokes... But it dawned on me that there wouldn't be much for folks to color if I filled everything up with ink, so I backed off and simplified much on the scenes you'll have to putter with and get your jollies. I very much hope you enjoy the book, and know I enjoyed the hell out of dredging it up for you.

Peace 'n love. — Uncle Glenny

CHADBOURNE

CHADBOURNE

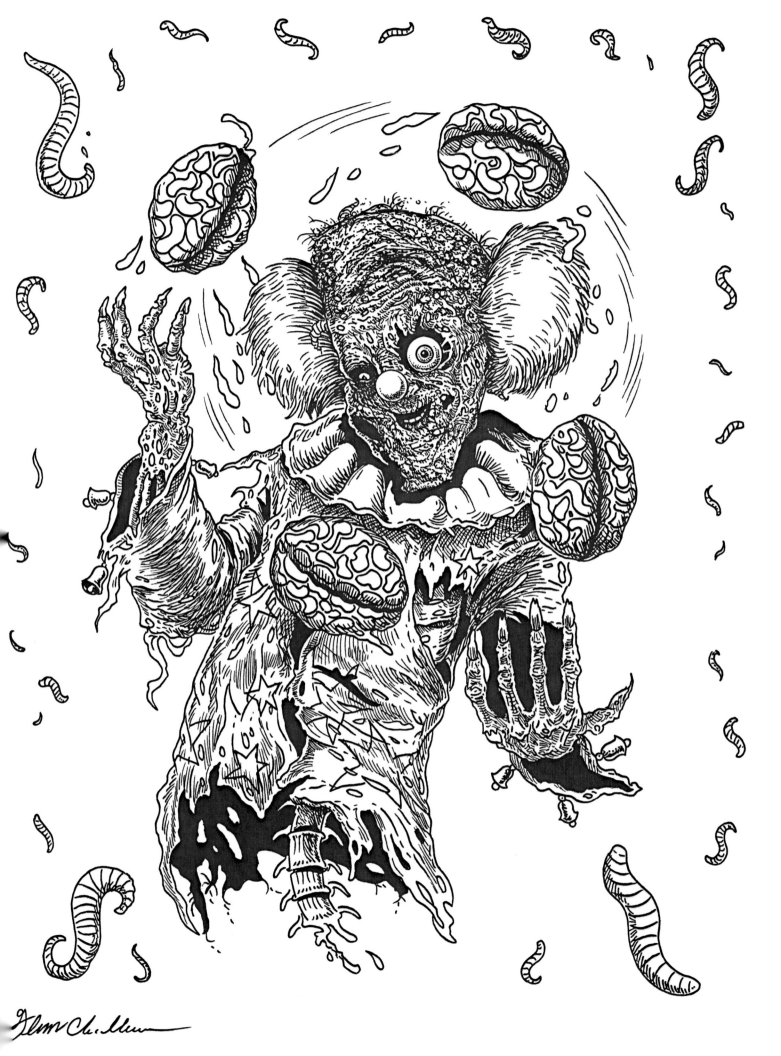

CHADBOURNE

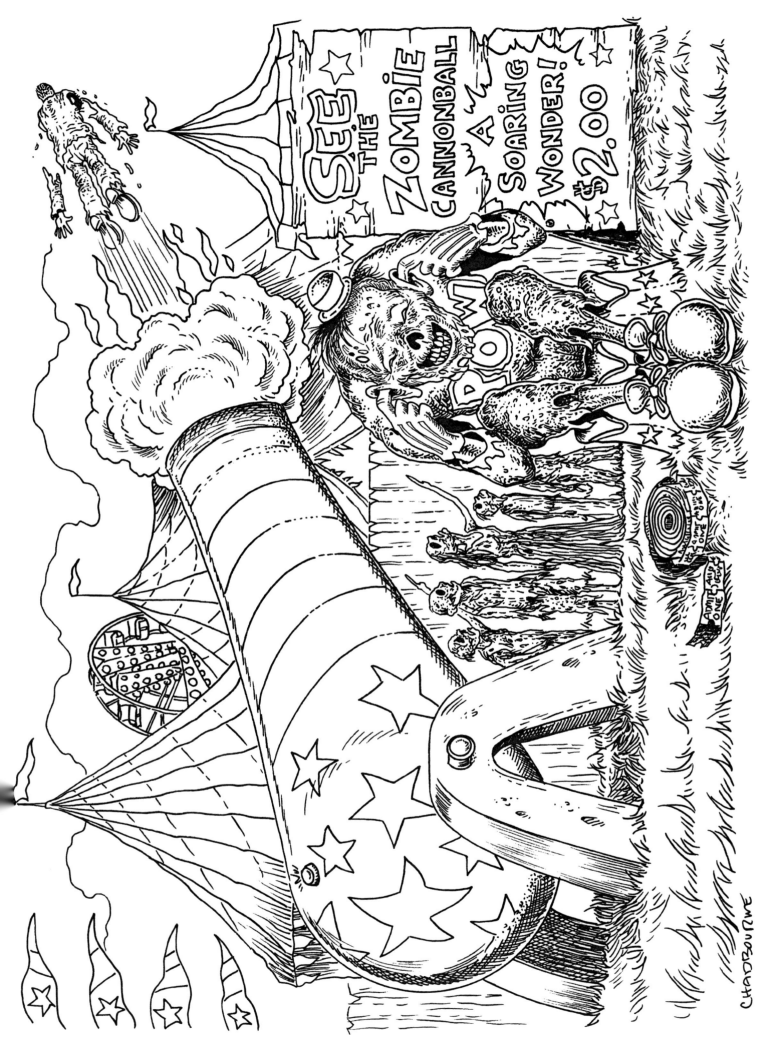

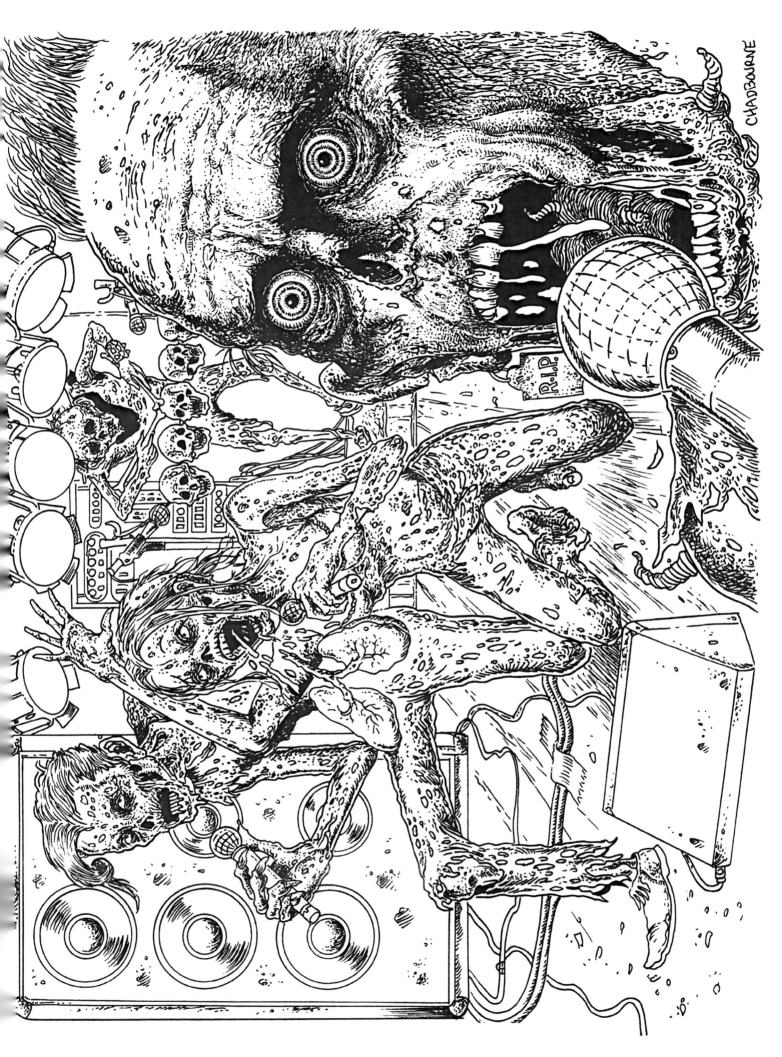

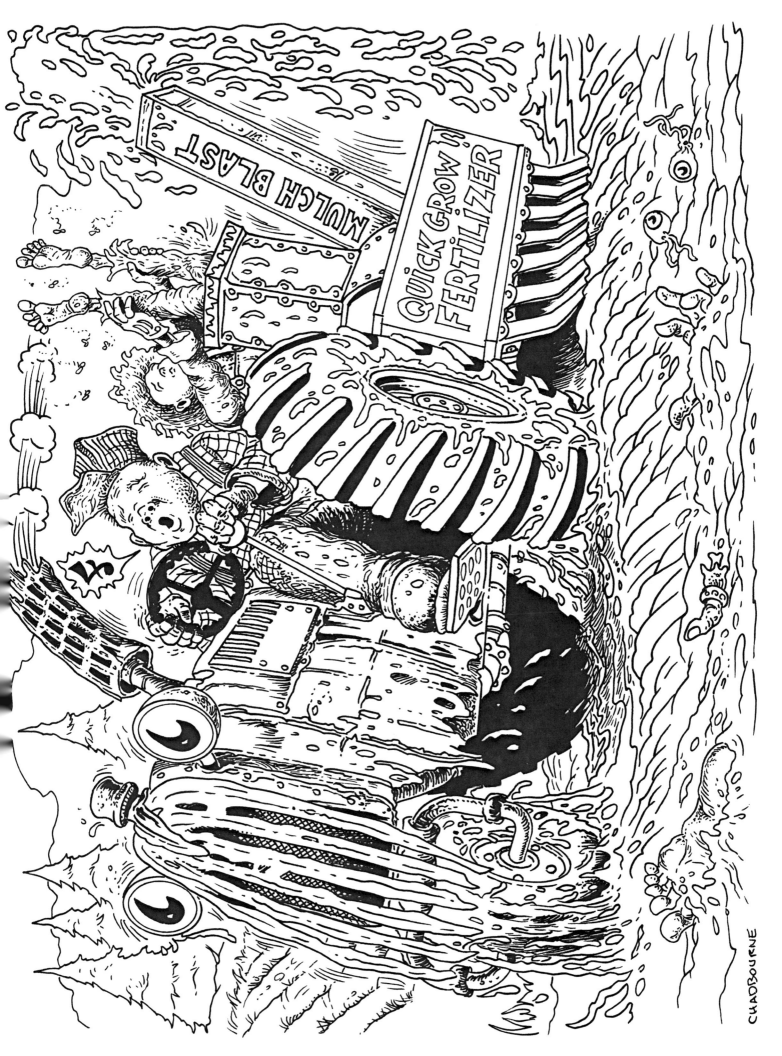

Glenn Chadbourne is well known in the horror world of writers, artists, and even in film (if you look close in Stephen King's *The Mist*, directed by Frank Darabont, you'll see Glenn's work). Artist to the stars, we all call him. Illustrator of so many novels and short story collections; including Joe Lansdale, Douglas Clegg, Rick Hautala, and especially Stephen King special editions. Too many to mention here, but he did create a beautiful two-volume set, *The Secretary of Dreams*, an illustrated short story collection that spans some of King's best short fiction. This project took him years to complete, and it was well worth the wait. With *Uncle Glenny's Zombie 'Pocalypse: An Adult Coloring Book*, this project took a year from start to finish. Based on concepts he co-created with publisher Dave Hinchberger, you can see and feel in these panels that horror and humor are truly part of a double-edged sword. In this case we've put that sword in as many of these zombie panels— or rather limbs— that could hold 'em. If you ever get a chance to meet ol' "Uncle Glenny," be sure to bring up some of the horror you've enjoyed in your life travels. Especially film, he loves a good, juicy, story, but don't hold back the gore... he wants to hear about every visceral, morsel. You never know, your description may end up in a future drawing.

Glenn frequently visits a beach near his home in Maine. A place he calls, "Pumpkin Cove." We spent some time down at the Cove with him. This little place is a beach with lots of rocks, not sand mind you, and dark forests that hang to the left and right of this dark water bay. I wouldn't want to be caught alone there at night, but you do get a feel of the world of "Uncle Glenny," while you're there, and from where he dredges up these ideas to insert in the stories he illustrates. Here's a chance to help color some of his unique work – the first of its kind – and he's put some fine Chadbourne style detail in some of these panels, to make it a an unparalleled experience.

Don't be surprised if something moves... during your quiet time with "Unk."

Glenn Chadbourne, Halloween 2016

devour everything. Whether its movies or comic books, novels or theater, Rock n' Roll to Jazz. Ever hear *Blue Belle Knoll*, by the Cocteau Twins? I can't understand a word they're saying, but the passion in this dark and beautiful piece speaks volumes. If it sounds good, I like it. I have so many interests that my niece calls me, "Mr. Entertainment." More so because I wanted to share the great, cool, stories I find in any medium. My family didn't always appreciate what I brought to them (*Dawn of the Dead* was too much for some), but they did enjoy the variety. Horror and Stephen King grabbed me by the boo-boo when I was knee high to the teen age. I think where it all really began was listening to the *CBS Mystery Theater* stories, on the car radio, late at night with my family on long car trips. All of my brothers, and sister, huddled in behind mom and dad in the station wagon, as the fateful sound of the drum roll theme, came echoing out of the tinny car speakers. I also think it was watching *Planet of the Apes* in the theater with my dad, at the age of 6, that really showed me what horror could have in store for us. Funny enough, it also intrigued me. At 10 I stumbled upon Jack Kirby's *Kamandi: The Last Boy on Earth*. He really impressed this young man, living off a dirt road in the wilds of southern Georgia.

Since then I had thoroughly became immersed in the world of Rock n' Roll. I've managed record stores, worked a decade for Polygram Records (a helluva an education), and became a publisher in my own right, as you can attest with the book you now hold in your hands. I also manage The Overlook Connection Bookstore, and its brother in horror, Stephen King Catalog. There's so much to see, read, and experience, and these days I get to share it with my lovely wife, LeeAnn, and our sons Johnathan, Clay, Ian, Kyle, and Trey. Trey, who has his own moniker for the walking dead: "Zambies."

Grab your favorite colors, turn to the first panel, and bring the dead... to life. One thing's for sure, don't turn your back on 'em.

Shamble on.

Dave Hinchberger, Halloween 2016

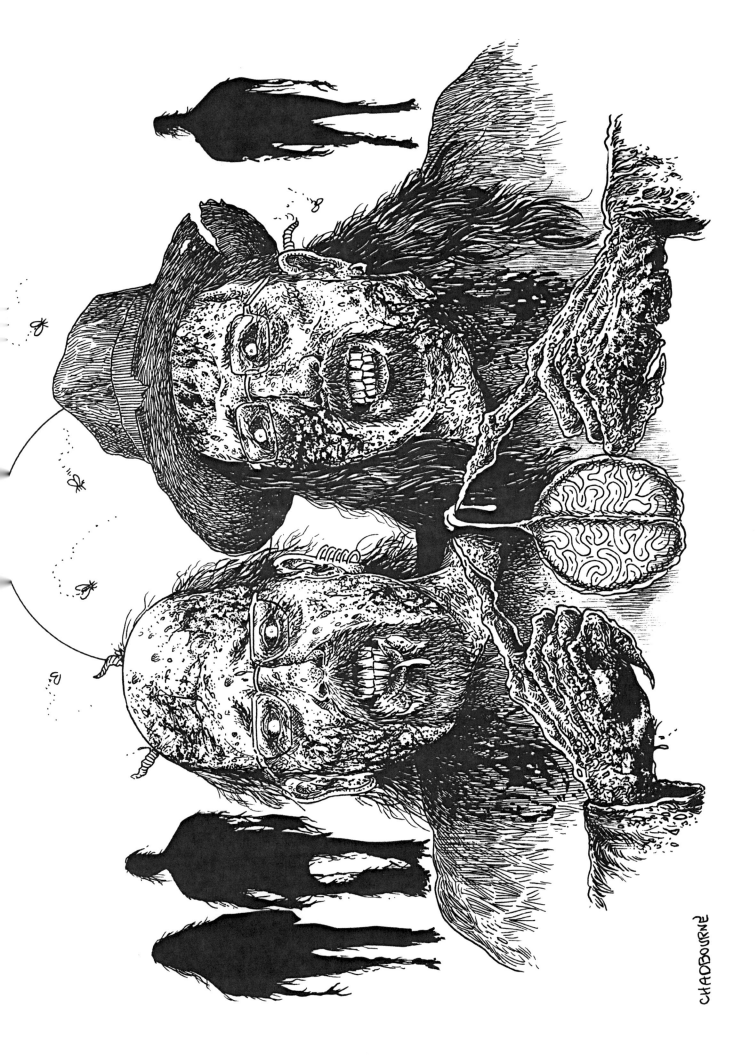

CHADBOURNE

Bookstore & Press of the Fantastique! Since 1987

Anthologies	Glenn Chadbourne Art	Overlook Connection Press
Art Books	Halloween	Poetry
Audio Books	Horror	Pulp Fiction
Biographies & Memoirs	Magazines	Science Fiction
Book Supplies	Merchandise	Screenplays
Clearance Items	Movies & TV	Slipcases
Collectibles & Ephemera	Music Books	Specialty Press
Comics	Music CD & CASS	StephenKingCatalog.com
Erotica	Mystery & Suspense	Video - DVD / VHS
Fantasy	Newspapers & Periodicals	Video Games
Fiction – General	Non-Fiction	Western

SIGN UP for the Overlook Connection Newsletter!
We will e-mail a 10% OFF Coupon on your First Order!

Weekly Updates, News, Art and Photos!
New and acquired items in Horror, Science Fiction, Fantasy & Mystery!

Celebrating Thirty Years 1987 – 2017 • OverlookConnection.Com

The Overlook Connection Bookstore and Press, and has been offering unique and specialized books and items since 1987. Specializing in: Stephen King, Horror, Science Fiction, Fantasy and Mystery. Signed limited editions, First editions, Video, Audio, Ephemera. Thousands of items!

Visit OverlookConnection.com and SIGN UP!

CATALOG.COM

Your Source for Everything... Stephen King! Since 1987

Collectibles & Ephemera	Joe Hill	Non-Fiction Titles
Comics	Magazines	Overlook Connection Press
Dark Tower & Fantasy	Stephen King Merchandise	Owen King
Horror	Mick Garris	Peter Straub
Mystery & Suspense	Movies & TV:	Stephen King Recommends
Science Fiction	Books / Scripts	Stephen King Slipcases
Short Fiction by Title	Music: CD & Cassette	Tabitha King
Glenn Chadbourne Items	Newspapers & Periodicals	Video: DVD & VHS

Stephen King Catalog.com is a subsidiary of The Overlook Connection Bookstore and Press, and has been offering unique and specialized books and items since 1987. Specializing in Stephen King, Horror, Science Fiction, Fantasy and Mystery. Signed limited editions, First editions, Video, Audio, Ephemera, et el. Thousands of items!

SIGN UP for the Stephen King Catalog Newsletter!

Weekly Updates, News, Art and Photos!
Announcements of new and rare items in the world of Stephen King!

Celebrating Thirty Years
1987 – 2017
StephenKingCatalog.Com

Visit StephenKingCatalog.com and SIGN UP!

CPSIA information can be obtained at www.ICGtesting.com
Printed in the USA
LVOW09s0516191016

509392LV00003B/3/P